D1582281

TIMELESS
LEGENDS

BRENDA RALPH LEWIS

Illustrated by Rob McCaig

BRIMAX BOOKS

CAMBRIDGE – ENGLAND

Introduction

Some three thousand years ago, the Greeks laid siege to Troy in a savage war that ended with the destruction of that city.

In the 6th century AD when Britain was invaded and occupied by Anglo-Saxons from northern Germany, a soldier called Artorius led the Britons against them.

In the year AD 778 Charlemagne, King of the Franks, was leading his army home from Spain when the Muslims attacked without warning. The entire rear section of Charlemagne's army was slaughtered.

Today, we watch television reports of battles and wars or read about them in the newspapers. Newspapers, television and radio – known as 'the media' report news about interesting people and unusual events. It was different in the days when there was no media and when most people could not read. News was transmitted by word of mouth in the form of stories like the ones in this book. Listening to them became a form of entertainment, and colourful details were invented for more enjoyment. Incidents were recorded a long time after their occurrence, the facts were frequently distorted – thus a legend was created – a story based upon a true event but enlarged upon by the imagination.

For example, four centuries after the Greek fight against Troy, the poet Homer told the story of the war in his epic poem *The Iliad*. Homer recounted how the Greeks had built a wooden horse with which they tricked the Trojans. This led to the destruction of Troy. Was there really a wooden horse? No one knows. However, the city of Troy was certainly destroyed.

Did Charlemagne, King of the Franks have a nephew called Roland and did Roland die bravely, fighting the Muslims in AD 778? Again, no one knows. The tragic story of Roland and his friend Oliver does show how greatly the virtues of Christian knights were admired in the 11th century AD, when their story was told in the Chanson de Roland (Song of Roland). These virtues were still greatly admired in the 14th century, when legends about King Arthur were very popular in the royal courts of Europe.

All these stories show that they contain something more than the bare facts about a person or an event. While you will read of many 'incredible' deeds and feats of magic in this book, do remember that behind them lie real-life happenings and real people who lived long, long ago.

Contents

The Wooden Horse of Troy   9

Rodrigo of Spain   16

Horatius at the Bridge   22

The Sword in the Stone   29

El Cid   36

William Tell   43

Roland and Oliver   50

Androclus and the Lion   58

Daedalus and Icarus   65

Sir Gawain and the Green Knight   72

© BRIMAX RIGHTS LTD. 1980. ALL RIGHTS RESERVED.
FIRST PUBLISHED IN GREAT BRITAIN BY
BRIMAX BOOKS, CAMBRIDGE, ENGLAND 1980
PRINTED IN ITALY.
ISBN O 86112 O68 X

The Wooden Horse of Troy

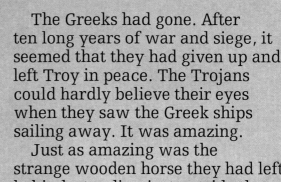

The Greeks had gone. After ten long years of war and siege, it seemed that they had given up and left Troy in peace. The Trojans could hardly believe their eyes when they saw the Greek ships sailing away. It was amazing.

Just as amazing was the strange wooden horse they had left behind, standing just outside the city walls. Was it a gift, the Trojans wondered, or was it a trick?

King Priam of Troy certainly suspected that the wooden horse was some kind of trick.

''The Greeks are the most cunning people on Earth'' Priam warned the Trojans. ''We must be very careful!''

Some of the Trojans, Priam knew, thought the horse was a sign of luck and victory. They wanted to drag it inside the walls of Troy. But Priam forbade them to do so until scouts had gone out to make sure the Greeks really *had* gone home.

The scouts armed themselves with swords and spears, in case they ran into a Greek ambush, then slipped out of the city to investigate the place where the Greeks had made their camp. There

was no ambush. What was more, there was no camp. When the Trojans reached it, they found the Greeks had burned their huts and tents. All that remained were a few heaps of blackened wreckage.

Then, while the scouts were picking their way through the ruined camp, they discovered one solitary Greek trying to hide behind some bushes. They dragged him out, kicking and shouting, and threw him on the ground.

''I beg you, do not kill me!'' he shrieked. ''Have mercy, kind sirs!'' Then, he started moaning. ''Oh, what misfortune has overtaken me! How unlucky I am!'' As he wailed and lamented, the Greek wept

profusely, so much so that the Trojans began to feel sorry for him.

''Who are you?'' they wanted to know. ''Why have the Greeks gone and left you behind?''

''My name is Sinon, and the Greeks hate me!'' the man sobbed. ''When they realised they could never capture Troy, they decided to go home, but they feared the gods would think them cowardly. So, they sought the advice of the oracle . . .''

''What did the oracle say?'' asked the Trojans curiously.

''The oracle said that the gods would not think the Greeks were cowards if they left behind one man as a sacrifice!" Sinon continued. "I am that sacrifice! Agamemnon, our leader, never liked me and as for Odysseus — the cunning, cruel man — he often said he wanted me killed! Now they have got their way!"

Sinon had stopped weeping now, and his tears had been replaced by fury and resentment. "They have betrayed me!" he cried. "Well, I will betray them!"

Sinon got to his feet and gripped one of the Trojans by the arm to make him pay close attention. "I will tell your king everything!" Sinon promised. "I know the secret of the wooden horse! I will reveal that secret, but only to King Priam!"

When Sinon mentioned the wooden horse, the Trojans pricked up their ears.

"Let's take this wretched Greek to Priam," the Trojans' leader decided.

"No, there's something odd going on," protested one of the scouts. "I don't trust this fellow — let's kill him now!" And he looked Sinon up and down with fierce, suspicious eyes. Sinon trembled and cringed before his gaze.

"Look at him!" the Trojan leader replied. "A man as terrified as this can be no danger to us. Besides, he has been betrayed and wants revenge. Such a man will always tell the truth!"

Sinon buried his face in his hands and started to make loud weeping noises once again. But behind his hands, unseen by the Trojans, Sinon was smiling. The plot was working! he thought. Everything was going exactly as

Odysseus had planned.

If the Trojans had any suspicions left about the departure of the Greeks, those suspicions soon vanished after Sinon told his story to Priam.

"The Greeks built the wooden horse as a gift for the goddess Athene" Sinon explained. "See the smile carved upon its face! The Greeks put it there to turn away Athene's anger. They were afraid she would send storms to wreck their ships as they sailed home . . . but here is the really cunning part of their scheme . . ."

"What? What?" asked Priam, longing to know. Everyone in Priam's court strained their ears to hear what Sinon was about to say.

"The Greeks were certain that you would burn the horse when you found it, thinking it was some trick on their part" Sinon went on. "If that happened, then the fury of Athene would fall on Troy and she would send a great thunderbolt and a cloud of fire to burn down this beautiful city!"

"So the wooden horse was a trick after all!" said King Priam "Why, then, we shall show the Greeks we are not fools here in Troy. We shall treat this horse with respect and honour, bring it inside the city and hold great celebrations round it!"

Priam clapped Sinon on the back in friendly fashion. "We have much to thank you for, Sinon," he smiled. "You shall join in our festivities as an honoured guest!"

Sinon chuckled secretly to himself. Of course, everything he had told King Priam had been a lie — except that the Greeks had, indeed, despaired of winning the war. That at least was true.

"If we cannot defeat the Trojans by force of arms," Odysseus told the other Greeks, "we must defeat them by cunning. Listen — I have a plan!"

When Agamemnon, the Greek leader, heard Odysseus' plan, he ordered his army to take their axes and chop down trees in the forest on nearby Mount Ida. Then, Epeius, the Greeks' most clever carpenter, got to work with his men. He cut the trees into thousands of planks and set about constructing the wooden horse. It took Epeius three days to complete it. As a finishing touch, Epeius carved the horse's mouth upwards, into a smile.

"There, my fine steed!" said Epeius, with satisfaction. "Before long you will have plenty to smile about!"

As soon as the horse was ready, Agamemnon gave orders for the Greek camp to be burned. Then, while the ships lying in the nearby harbour were made ready for sea, Odysseus, Epeius and a number of other Greek warriors donned their armour and wrapped their swords and spears tightly in their cloaks.

When it grew dark, they climbed up a long ladder and entered the hollow belly of the horse, through a trap door in one side. When everyone was inside, Epeius pulled up the trap door and bolted it. There they sat, in the darkness, holding their weapons tightly so that they did not rattle while the wooden horse was hauled to a spot just outside the walls of Troy.

Then Agamemnon and the rest of the Greeks, all except Sinon, embarked into their ships and sailed away. Sinon was left behind in the camp, waiting for the

Trojans to come and find him.

The Trojans were so completely convinced by Sinon's story that they flung open the city gates and hauled the wooden horse inside. A crowd followed behind singing, dancing and cheering.

"They think they have won the war!" Sinon thought as he watched the merrymaking. "They will soon discover how they have lost it!"

At length, the Trojans grew tired and started to go home. Sinon stayed behind. When the last Trojan had disappeared, he ran swiftly to where the wooden horse stood and gave three raps on one of its legs.

"At last!" murmured Odysseus in the darkness of the horse's belly. "The time has come for action!"

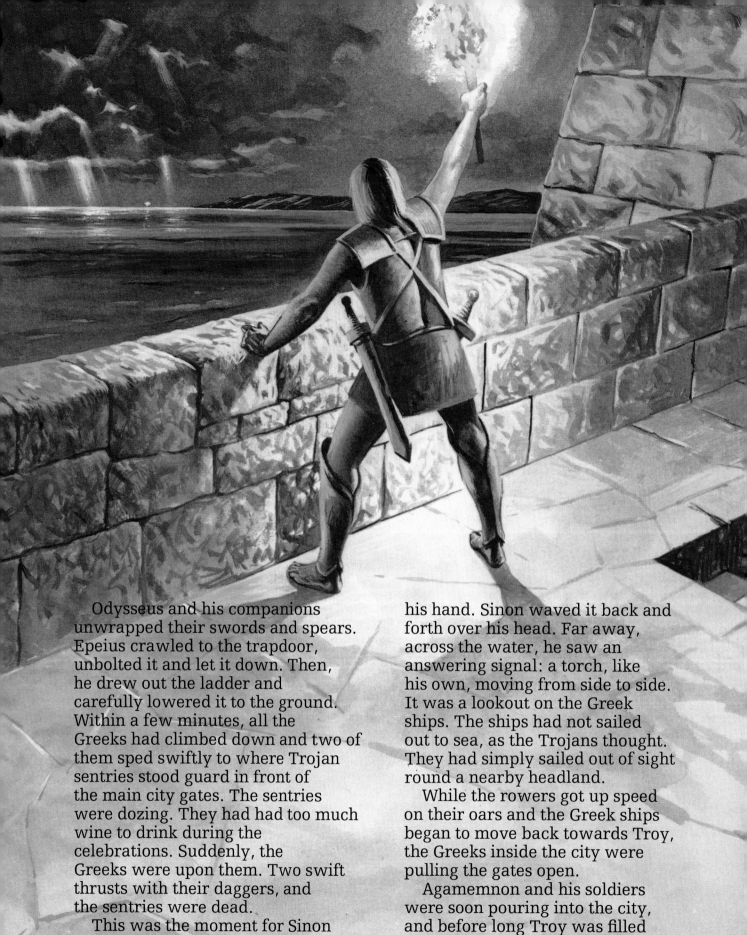

Odysseus and his companions unwrapped their swords and spears. Epeius crawled to the trapdoor, unbolted it and let it down. Then, he drew out the ladder and carefully lowered it to the ground. Within a few minutes, all the Greeks had climbed down and two of them sped swiftly to where Trojan sentries stood guard in front of the main city gates. The sentries were dozing. They had had too much wine to drink during the celebrations. Suddenly, the Greeks were upon them. Two swift thrusts with their daggers, and the sentries were dead.

This was the moment for Sinon to climb the staircase to the ramparts. He carried a torch in his hand. Sinon waved it back and forth over his head. Far away, across the water, he saw an answering signal: a torch, like his own, moving from side to side. It was a lookout on the Greek ships. The ships had not sailed out to sea, as the Trojans thought. They had simply sailed out of sight round a nearby headland.

While the rowers got up speed on their oars and the Greek ships began to move back towards Troy, the Greeks inside the city were pulling the gates open.

Agamemnon and his soldiers were soon pouring into the city, and before long Troy was filled with shouts and screams and the crackle of burning buildings.

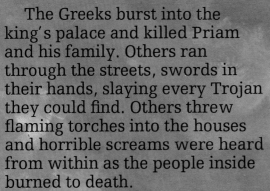

The Greeks burst into the king's palace and killed Priam and his family. Others ran through the streets, swords in their hands, slaying every Trojan they could find. Others threw flaming torches into the houses and horrible screams were heard from within as the people inside burned to death.

Soon, the streets of Troy were strewn with the bodies of the dead and the whole city was covered in thick black smoke. Men, women and children were running about shrieking in terror, trying to hide from the Greeks. But there was no escape. They were killed or bound in chains and dragged down to the Greek ships.

By the time dawn came, the once splendid city of Troy was nothing but a smoking, silent, ruin. No one there was left alive.

Only one structure remained standing in the city when the Greeks finally left, carrying off their prisoners and all the gold and treasure they had looted. That structure was the wooden horse. Untouched by the flames, it stood in the square, still smiling the triumphant smile which Epeius had carved upon its face.

Rodrigo of Spain

King Rodrigo of Spain was very suspicious. He had never heard anything as ridiculous as the story the two strange old men had come to tell him. They were an odd sight, clad in long white robes, with stars and moons embroidered all over them.

They looked like magicians or sorcerers. From their girdles, there hung bunches of rusty old keys. These, they said, were the keys to padlocks which Spanish kings had fixed to the door of the Enchanted Tower in past years.

According to the two old men, each king had woven a spell around his padlocks, to keep the Muslims from invading Christian Spain. Now, the two old men wanted King Rodrigo to do the same.

"Enchanted Tower, magic spells, padlocks . . ." King Rodrigo thought. "I don't believe a word of it!"

Still, that Tower did sound interesting. It was made of marble and the rich jewel jasper. With all that wealth outside, who knew what treasure lay inside?

"Very well," said Rodrigo. "Take me to the Tower! But I will not fix a padlock until I have entered it and seen what is inside!"

At this, the two old men started wailing and wringing their hands.

"No, no your Majesty!" they cried in great anxiety. "No one must enter the Tower! It is forbidden. If you enter the Tower, the Muslims will be sure to invade Spain . . . We beg you, your Majesty, we entreat you, do not go into the Tower!"

"Nonsense, babbling nonsense!" Rodrigo replied. He rose from his throne, and walked across to the two old men. Roughly, he poked one of them in the ribs. "I know what you are doing!" Rodrigo snarled at him. "You have hidden treasure in the Tower, and you want me to put another lock on it so that it will be even safer than it is now!"

The old men raised their hands in horror.

"No, no it's not true! We have never been inside the Tower! We told you — disaster awaits if anyone enters the Tower, even you, your Majesty!"

Rodrigo looked very angry.

"You are lying! I'll hear no more of this nonsense. You will take me to the Tower and you will unlock it for me. I will see what is inside, and if I find you have been keeping treasure from me, both of you shall die!"

Immediately, Rodrigo ordered horses to be saddled and together with the old men and two of his knights, he galloped out of his palace and rode swiftly to the Tower.

It was beautiful. Tall and straight, with brightly shining walls, covered in red, yellow and brown jasper. Rodrigo gazed at it entranced. He rode round the Tower several times, wondering at its beauty and more sure than ever that lying inside he would find fabulous wealth in gold, silver and jewels.

Rodrigo made the old men dismount from their horses. The two of them were shaking all over.

"Unlock the Tower!" Rodrigo ordered them. "Stop that noise!" he growled as the two old men broke into loud wailing cries.

Once more, Rodrigo commanded them to be silent, but they went on crying and moaning and wringing their hands.

Rodrigo was becoming very impatient. These two old fools were so terrified, they might take a month to undo all those padlocks. There were at least a dozen of them. Rodrigo turned to his two knights. "Break it open!" he commanded. "Your axes and swords should be able to break those padlocks!"

It was hard work. Half an hour passed before one of the knights finally managed to break the last chain across the door of the Tower. It fell away and Rodrigo hurried

forward to turn the handle and open the door.

Slowly, the door creaked inwards. It was very dark inside the Tower, and for a moment, even Rodrigo felt afraid. However, with the thought of the treasure inside, his fear vanished and he marched through the doorway and into the entrance hall of the Tower.

For a moment, Rodrigo could see nothing. Then, as his eyes grew accustomed to the dim light, he saw gold and silver glittering on a great marble table in the centre of the hall. He gasped. The table was covered with gold and silver coins.

Rodrigo rushed towards the table, followed by his two knights. The two old men remained outside, still shaking with anxiety and fear. Rodrigo picked up two handfuls of coins and let them trickle through his fingers. It was a wonderful feeling.

In the centre of the table, there stood a marble urn. More treasure lay inside, Rodrigo was sure.

Swiftly, he pushed aside the lid of the urn, and plunged his hand in. But instead of jewels or more coins, all Rodrigo could feel was a piece of parchment. He drew it out, and rather mystified, unrolled it.

It was a picture, painted in brilliant colours. The picture showed a line of horsemen, bearing long spears in their hands. The horsemen were brown-skinned, just like the people across the Straits of Gibraltar, in Morocco. Like them, they had long, thick, shaggy hair and from their belts hung strange curved swords, just like the ones the Muslims used in battle.

''Look, your Majesty,'' said one of the knights. ''There is something written below the picture.'' He began to read and as he did so, his voice started to tremble. "Behold, when the door of this Tower is forced open by violence and the spell contained in this urn is broken, then the people painted on this picture will invade Spain . . ." The knight faltered, unable to read on for a moment. Then he continued:

". . . then the people painted on this picture will invade Spain, overthrow the throne of her king and conquer the whole country!"

King Rodrigo had turned very pale. He had expected to find treasure, not this dreadful prophecy of doom and disaster. He looked again at the picture and its brown-skinned horsemen and he began to shiver.

Then, suddenly, as Rodrigo watched, the picture came to life. The brown-skinned horsemen were galloping, waving their spears in the air . . . Behind them, Rodrigo saw a flag with a star and a crescent on it: the flag of the Muslims! A violent battle was being fought in the picture. Rodrigo recognised Christian knights of

Spain, struggling against the horsemen, and falling from their saddles one by one.

There was one horse in particular which caught Rodrigo's attention. It belonged to the Christian army and it was snow-white in colour. On its back was a saddle decorated with beautiful jewels. The jewels were glittering in the sunshine. But where was the rider? He was nowhere to be seen.

Rodrigo let out a cry of fear. He knew that beautiful snow-white horse. He knew that bejewelled saddle. Frantically, Rodrigo searched the picture for the rider of the snow-white horse, but he could not find him.

Suddenly, Rodrigo realised what that meant, and panic took hold of

him. He turned and rushed out of the Tower. As he ran through the doorway, he nearly fell over two bodies lying just outside it. They were the bodies of the two old men. They were dead.

Rodrigo did not stop. He

leaped onto his horse, and with his knights following close behind, galloped away from the Tower at high speed. As they raced down the hillside, they heard a deafening explosion. They turned, to see the Tower engulfed in blood-red flames, and clouds of black smoke. When the smoke cleared, the Tower was gone. In its place was a heap of molten ruins.

For years afterwards, King Rodrigo tried hard to forget the Tower and the dreadful things he saw in the moving picture. In particular, Rodrigo tried to forget the snow-white horse without a rider. To help himself forget, Rodrigo went hunting, or gave great banquets in his palace at Toledo. He made long journeys through his kingdom and held splendid tournaments where his knights fought mock battles against each other.

Nothing helped. Rodrigo could never forget the Tower and the dreadful prophecy he had seen there. In any case, how could Rodrigo forget when every year brought dreadful news from North Africa across the Mediterranean Sea. Every year, hordes of warrior Muslims advanced westwards along the North African coast. First, Rodrigo heard they were in Libya, then they were through the Atlas Mountains, and were pouring into Morocco. Finally, Rodrigo received the news he most dreaded to hear. The Muslim fleet was crossing the Straits of Gibraltar, and making for the coast of Spain.

At once, King Rodrigo gathered his army of knights, nobles and thousands of foot soldiers. This great army set out to meet the Muslims on a battleground near the River Guadalete.

As soon as Rodrigo saw the huge Muslim hordes, he knew the battle was lost.

"Brown skins, long, shaggy hair, those long spears and curved swords," he murmured to himself as he looked at the Muslims. "They are all like the horsemen in the picture . . . the picture was a portent!"

He was right. The battle was hard-fought, just as it was in the picture. Yet however hard they fought, the Spanish knights could not overcome the Muslims. One by one they were killed and toppled from their saddles to the ground.

Tarik, the Muslim leader, searched for King Rodrigo. He soon found him, for no one had a snow-white horse like the King of Spain. No one had a jewelled saddle like the one on which Rodrigo sat.

Tarik pushed his way through the mass of struggling soldiers and rearing, whinnying horses.

"Fight to the death, Rodrigo!" Tarik cried. Thrusting his sword in front of him, he galloped towards the Spanish king.

"To the death, then!" Rodrigo shouted back, but almost as soon as the words were out of his mouth, Tarik's sword had plunged through his neck.

Rodrigo died at once, and his body tumbled down from his bejewelled saddle. Startled to find Rodrigo's weight suddenly gone from her back, his horse took fright. As she galloped away, the sun gleamed off her snow-white coat and the fine leather of her empty saddle. Its jewels glittered in the rays of the sun.

Horatius at the Bridge

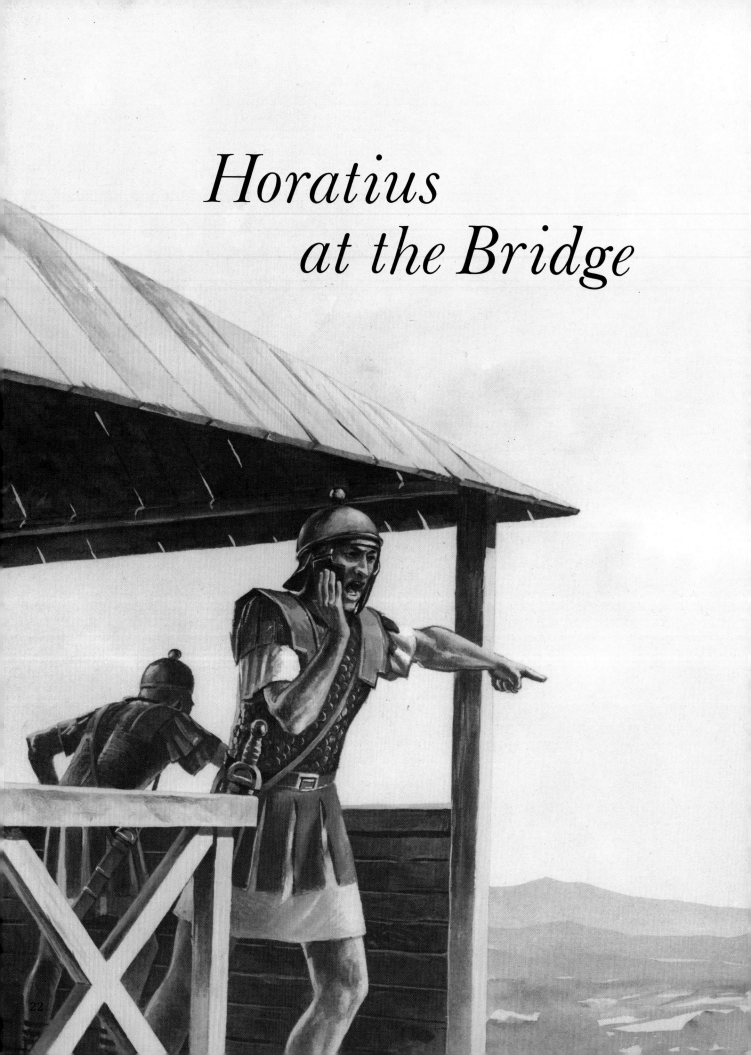

"They're coming! They're coming!" The sentry's cry of warning echoed down from the watchtower high above the city of Rome. The sentry hurried down the winding staircase to report to the commander of the Roman army, Lucius Junius Brutus.

"A thousand, perhaps fifteen hundred men . . ." the sentry told Lucius breathlessly. "Spearmen, swordsmen and horsemen! A league away, I should say — perhaps three thousand paces!"

Lucius turned to face the rows of soldiers who stood before him, armed, armoured and ready to fight.

"You have heard the news!" Lucius told them. "King Tarquinius and his ally, King Porsenna of Clusium, are coming with a great army. Tarquinius wants his throne back — he wants to become King of Rome again and rule us as harshly as he did before! Will we allow him to succeed?"

"No! No!" The soldiers' reply came in a great roaring shout. "We have had enough of kings! We threw Tarquinius out of Rome — he can stay out!"

Lucius smiled. He felt proud to be the leader of an army with such courage and spirit. Lucius knew that his commanders — young men like Horatius and Gaius Mucius — were fine leaders, and the troops they were to lead were great fighters. What more could any leader of an army ask?

Still, thought Lucius, it would not be easy to defeat Tarquinius and Porsenna.

One thing was certain. The enemy must not get across the Pons Sublicius (Sublican Bridge) over the River Tiber. If that happened Rome could be in great danger and its earth ramparts might not be enough to stop Tarquinius from entering the city.

That was why Lucius had ordered Horatius and his men to stand guard on the Sublican. If anyone could keep that bridge safe and secure, it was Horatius.

Suddenly, a dreadful howling sound reached Lucius' ears. A moment later, a huge boulder came thudding down to earth, and landed about twenty paces outside the ramparts. The attack had begun and the enemy was using stone-throwing and probably other siege machines as well.

"To your posts!" Lucius yelled to his army. He drew his short sword from its scabbard and raised it above his head. ''Fight to the death for Rome!'' he cried.

As the soldiers ran to station themselves along the ramparts, Lucius nodded to Horatius and Gaius Mucius. It was the signal the two young Roman commanders had been waiting for. Horatius clasped Gaius by the hand.

''Death to Tarquinius!'' Horatius said firmly. ''The gods preserve you, Gaius, my friend!''

''The gods preserve you, Horatius!'' Gaius replied. ''You greatly need their protection!''

Gaius was right, Horatius thought as he led his fifty men out of the city, and down the Palatine Hill towards the Tiber and the Sublican Bridge. The gods of Rome would have to fight very hard on his side, for defending the bridge was a truly perilous task.

It had no proper defences. All Horatius and his men could do was to stand and fight with the River Tiber and the bridge behind them.

The bridge was made of thick, strong wooden planks. Many times since it was first built by Ancius, fourth king of Rome, the bridge had been swept away by floods. This was not one of those times, however.

The Sublican stood strong and firm as Horatius marched across, and the river flowed quietly beneath it.

''Spearmen, over there — swordsmen on this side!'' Horatius quickly gave orders to his men to position themselves. He concentrated half his force at the end of the bridge, and stationed the rest along the banks of the river on either side.

The army of Tarquinius and Porsenna was very close now, so close that Horatius could see the designs emblazoned on their shields. Horatius tried to count the number of enemy soldiers, but there were too many of them.

Suddenly, Horatius heard the whistling sound of a spear slicing through the air towards him. He jumped aside to avoid it and the spearhead struck the bridge and stuck there. A swordsman was

making straight for him, yelling fearful war cries and brandishing his sword in the air. Horatius leapt forward, thrusting his own sword up and the two swords met with a loud metallic clang. There came a scraping sound as the enemy whipped his sword away. He wielded it again to strike another blow at Horatius, but before he could do so Horatius lunged forward and plunged his sword into the man's chest. The man gave a horrible gurgling cry and crumpled to the ground.

Quickly, Horatius looked round. Along the bank of the river, fierce struggles were going on, with two enemy soldiers or more lunging at each Roman with swords and spears.

The air was filled with the sounds and the screams of battle, the clash of sword on sword, the whistle of javelins flying through the air and, from some distance in front of Horatius, the heavy clank and thud of the enemy's siege machines. Several times, Horatius saw huge boulders and stones flying through the air above his head. The boulders fell into the river behind him, but Horatius realised what the enemy was trying to do.

"They're trying to kill us all quickly — one of those boulders could crush five men," Horatius thought anxiously.

For the moment, the aim of the men working the siege machines was not quite accurate. All their missiles fell into the Tiber or on the opposite bank of the river.

But if they shortened their range a bit or pulled their siege machines back a little . . .

Then, it happened. A great

boulder came whistling over and hit its target — half a dozen of Horatius' spearmen who were holding a group of enemy soldiers at bay with their javelins. There was a dreadful crash, and terrible screams as the spearmen were struck and crushed down onto the ground by the enormous weight.

Suddenly, Horatius smelled burning. He looked quickly along the river bank. Several Romans, their clothing ablaze, were leaping into the water in an attempt to put out the flames. It was obvious what had happened. The siege machines were now being used to fling flaming torches.

But now, Horatius saw something even more horrifying. Not one of his fifty men was left standing. Their bodies were strewn on the ground or floating in the river or sprawled out on the banks sloping down to the water.

Horatius was alone — the only man left out of his entire force!

"Very well, then!" Horatius cried. "If that's how the gods have decreed, I'll defend the bridge alone!"

Horatius snatched up a javelin lying nearby, and leapt a few paces back along the bridge. There he stood, sword in one hand, javelin in the other, with his shield looped firmly round one arm.

"One man against five hundred!" Horatius snarled at the crowd of enemy soldiers in front of him. "But that one man is a Roman! You shall not cross this bridge, I swear it!"

The enemy soldiers were so startled that for a moment they did not move. Then, one of them began to laugh.

"He's mad!" he yelled. "Imagine one man against all of us!"

Other soldiers took up the cry and started to yell insults at Horatius. "You're a lunatic!" they shouted. "You'd best jump in the river and cool your crazy head!"

Horatius stood his ground, his eyes dark with fury and determination. "You shall not cross!" he growled. He lunged at one enemy soldier who was just about to jump onto the bridge in front of him. The enemy retreated hastily, back to the safety of the crowd at the end of the bridge.

Horatius realised that the soldiers were afraid of him. They thought he was out of his mind, and feared to fight against a madman. It could not go on for much longer, though. Someone would throw a spear or a sword, and that would be the end.

Fortunately, Gaius Mucius had seen what was happening from the ramparts above. He ordered his men to open the gates so that they could go to Horatius' aid.

"Fetch some axes!" Gaius ordered. "There's only one way to save Horatius — and Rome. We've got to chop that bridge down!"

Horatius' position was getting very dangerous now.

As Gaius and his men rushed out of the gates and started running down towards the bridge, one of the enemy soldiers lunged at Horatius with his sword. Horatius managed to twist the sword out of the man's hand and throw him back, but if the enemy came at him in force, Gaius knew it would take only seconds for Horatius to be overwhelmed.

Reaching the bridge, Gaius started to hack away at the planks that held it to the river bank. Four or five others were doing the same and gradually, the planks were cracking and splitting apart. Horatius felt the bridge vibrate and as the first four planks were chopped through, the whole bridge began to sway. The enemy soldiers saw what was happening and drew back from their end of the bridge, fearful of being thrown into the water when it collapsed.

Gaius and his men kept chopping away at the planks, turning the blades of the axes to split the wood, till only one plank was left. By now, the bridge was swaying alarmingly. Gaius gave a terrific swipe with his axe and as the blade chopped through the last plank, the bridge suddenly tipped sideways. With a great creaking, groaning and splintering it toppled down towards the river.

Horatius was flung off. He

plunged into the water and disappeared, weighed down by his heavy armour. For one dreadful moment, Gaius thought Horatius had drowned. Then suddenly, there he was, up on the surface again and swimming strongly towards the river bank. Gaius rushed forward and, grabbing Horatius' hand, hauled him out of the water.

"There!" Horatius told Gaius, pointing to the confused horde of enemy soldiers who were staring stupidly at the wrecked bridge.

"I told them they wouldn't get across!"

All along the ramparts, the Romans were cheering and shouting out Horatius' name. When he came back into the city, Lucius Junius Brutus was there to congratulate him for his magnificent deed. Lucius placed a laurel wreath on Horatius' head and told him:

"This is the mark of a hero of Rome! You will be among Rome's greatest heroes, Horatius! Tarquinius will never come back now that he has Romans like you to contend with!"

Lucius was right. After seeing what had happened at the Sublican Bridge, King Porsenna, Tarquinius' ally, became afraid to fight against the Romans. Porsenna went home to Clusium, leaving Tarquinius with no soldiers to fight for him. Tarquinius had lost his throne for ever, and never again were the Romans ruled by kings.

The Sword in the Stone

No one knew how the square slab of marble-stone came to be in the churchyard. One moment, there was nothing there but empty ground. The next moment, or so it seemed, the huge slab simply appeared. And what a stone it was! It looked as if it had been hewn from the side of a mountain. On top of it stood a great iron anvil, and buried deep in the anvil was the long, sharp, shining steel blade of a sword.

It was Christmas day, and the knights of King Uther Pendragon had come to pray in the church. For this one day, they seemed willing to set aside their constant quarrelling over which of them should be King of Britain. The rivalry had been going on ever since Uther died, with no son to succeed him. It was violent rivalry. Each knight was willing to kill all the others in order to possess the throne.

Merlin the Magician sighed as he looked round at the brutish faces of the knights in the church. It was tragic that men like these should be the leaders of the Britons, for they were more interested in their own ambitions than in the welfare of their nation. While Uther's knights were squabbling, Britain was in a terrible plight. Year by year, fierce Anglo-Saxon invaders were conquering more and more of the land. If the Britons were to stop them, they must have a king, but a king acknowledged by all as their true and only rightful ruler. That was the purpose of the sword in the stone. It was the only means by which Merlin could show the people who their king really was.

When the knights left the church, they spotted the stone straight away. At once, they crowded round it and ran their fingers over the hard surface of the stone. They looked with amazement and admiration at the mighty steel sword. It was the sort of sword that could kill all rivals, and there was not a man there who did not long to possess it.

Then, one of the knights saw the words carved in golden lettering along the side of the stone.

They read: "Whoso pulleth out this sword from this stone and anvil is the true-born King of all Britain!"

As soon as they saw this message, the knights rushed forward, only too eager to pull the sword out of the anvil. They pushed and shoved and shouted, demanding to be the first.

Eventually, one knight barged in front and grasped the hilt. He pulled. The sword did not move. He heaved and hauled, using all his strength. Still it would not budge. Disgusted and disappointed the knight gave up. He was followed by another and another, all of them straining to get the sword out until they turned blue in the face with the effort. But the sword did not move an inch.

The knights were furious. Merlin was standing nearby, watching them with that mysterious smile of his. The knights shook their fists at him. "This is one of your tricks, Merlin!" they raged. "You've put a spell on this sword!"

"No trick, Sir Knight!" Merlin replied quietly. "It simply means that none of you is the true-born King of Britain!"

"Where is he, then?" growled one of the knights, a large man with a nasty look on his face. "If I ever get my hands on him, I'll fight him for the throne — true-born king or no!"

"You may yet get your chance, if you dare to take it," Merlin told him. "There will be a great tournament here on New Year's Day. Knights have been summoned from far and near to joust and fight with swords — and all will try to draw the sword from this stone. We shall see if any can do so!"

In the week between Christmas Day and New Year, the roads were filled with splendid processions of knights, all mounted on great strong horses, and followed by their squires and servants. All were heading towards the great tournament. All hoped to draw the sword from the stone and so be proclaimed King of Britain.

Among the knights was Sir Ector and his son Sir Kay, and with them came Sir Ector's younger son, Arthur.

Arthur was only sixteen, too young to be a knight, so he could not take part in the jousting, but he could assist his father and brother and look after their weapons and their horses.

By the time New Year's Day dawned, the field where the tournament was to be held was crowded with bell-shaped tents of all brilliant colours. From the top of each one, there fluttered the flag of the knight who owned it, each flag with its own special pattern and design. Arthur sat by the side of the field and looked round excitedly. He was always happiest when he was among fine horses and brave fighting men, and loved the noise and bustle and thrills of the tournament.

Suddenly, Arthur saw his brother Sir Kay, riding towards him. Sir Kay seemed to be in a great hurry.

"I've left my second sword behind at our lodgings!" he told Arthur. "A stupid thing — how could I have forgotten it? Will you run and get it for me?"

Arthur scrambled quickly to his feet. He loved and admired his elder brother and liked doing things for him.

"Of course I will!" Arthur replied. He ran off to the house nearby where he and his brother and father were staying while the tournament lasted. Arthur soon reached the door of the house, but found, to his dismay, that it was locked. He banged on the door and shouted, but no one was there.

"Everyone must be at the tournament!" thought Arthur. "What shall I do? My brother Kay must have his sword!"

Suddenly Arthur remembered the sword in the stone. It was still there, in the churchyard, for none of the knights had succeeded in drawing it out.

Quickly, Arthur ran to the churchyard, clambered up onto the great stone, and pulled the sword out of the anvil. It was very beautiful. Arthur admired its fine broad blade and the way it shone in the brilliant winter sunshine. "Sir Kay will be very pleased with this!" Arthur thought, turning the blade from side to side so that it sparkled in the light.

At that moment, Arthur had forgotten all about the message carved on the side of the stone. But Sir Kay and Sir Ector had not forgotten. When they saw Arthur coming towards them waving the great sword to show he had done as Sir Kay had asked, they gasped with astonishment.

"Here, brother Kay!" Arthur panted, somewhat out of breath with all the running about he had done. "Here is a fine sword for you . . ."

"Where did you get this?" Sir Ector asked Arthur.

"From the churchyard — it was sticking in the anvil," Arthur explained, suddenly worried to see the serious expression on his father's face. "Have I done wrong, Father?" he asked anxiously.

Sir Ector shook his head and put a hand on his young son's shoulder. His hand, Arthur noticed was trembling. "No, you have not done wrong, Arthur" Sir Ector said. "But let us go to the churchyard and see you take the sword from the stone again!"

"Put the sword back in the stone, Arthur," Sir Ector commanded him, when they reached the churchyard. The sword slid into the anvil smoothly and easily.

Sir Ector beckoned to Sir Kay.

"Try to take it out," he told him. Sir Kay grasped the hilt and pulled.

He pulled again. He heaved at it a third time. The sword seemed firmly stuck.

"What is the matter, brother Kay?" Arthur asked. "Why can't you move the sword? Look — it's easy!" And he reached up, grasped the sword hilt and slid the blade out of the anvil with one swift movement.

Suddenly, to Arthur's amazement, his father and brother knelt on the ground before him.

They were bowing their heads to him in reverence.

"What are you doing?" Arthur cried. "Why do you kneel to me?"

"Because you are the true-born King of Britain," Sir Ector said. "And I am honoured to pledge you my allegiance and to serve you!"

Arthur was dumbfounded. "I? A King?" he gasped. "There must be some mistake!"

"No, Arthur," said a voice behind him. "There is no mistake."

It was Merlin. He had been watching everything from the shadow of the church door. Now, the

magician came forward, holding a
magnificent gold scabbard and belt.
''Take this, Arthur,'' Merlin said.
''It is yours. I have waited many
years to give it to you, for I have
known ever since you were born that
you, and no other, are the true-
born King of Britain!''

Arthur was unable to speak.
He simply gazed, wonderstruck at
the shining gold scabbard, turning
it over and over in his hands.
Merlin watched him, and for a
moment felt sad that such a young
boy should be burdened with so

awesome a destiny. As King of
Britain, Merlin knew that Arthur
would not find it easy to bring
peace to his people after so many
years of rivalry and fighting.
And the Anglo Saxons, whom Arthur
would have to fight, were not easy
foes to overcome. But all that lay
in the future. Now was the time
for celebrations.

''Come!'' said Merlin. ''We must
tell the people that their King
has made himself known at last.
They have waited a long time to
hear this gladdest of glad news!''

El Cid

In the summer of 1099, a great sadness filled the city of Valencia in Spain. People walked through the streets, heads down, hardly exchanging a word with each other. There was none of the normal cheerful chatter and noise in the markets. At the inns, men sat drinking their tankards of wine or beer in melancholy silence. The innkeepers, who were usually full of good stories and good cheer, had no tales or jokes to tell; they went about their work with long, morose faces.

If anyone asked a question, it was always the same one: "Any news yet?" The reply might be "No!" or simply a sad shake of the head. What the people of Valencia feared most was the day when the answer to that question would be "Yes!" For that would mean that El Cid, Roderigo Diaz de Vivar, ruler of Valencia, was dead. El Cid was an old man, worn out by more than thirty years of fighting battles and hard campaigning. With his armies, El Cid had marched long gruelling distances in the burning heat of the Spanish summer. Many times, he had been wounded, only to ignore his injuries and inspire his men by fighting alongside them. Now, all those years of hardship had taken their toll. El Cid was dying. Worse still for the people of Valencia, their Muslim enemies were gleefully anticipating his death, for then they could make their final attack on Valencia and capture it.

The Muslims had themselves given Roderigo Diaz his nickname of "El Cid". In Arabic, the Muslim language, it meant "Lord". Roderigo's own Christian armies had another name for him: "Campeador", which meant "winner of battles". Both Muslims and Christians agreed the El Cid was the greatest soldier in Spain. At a time when the two sides were struggling for control of the country, the armies led by El Cid had prevailed in one battle after another, and helped Christian rule to spread through northern Spain. After 1094, El Cid had conquered and ruled a large area of eastern Spain, in the province of Valencia.

El Cid was so successful that Muslim soldiers used to tremble if they even heard his name. Their leaders came to realise they could never win victories over the Christians while El Cid lived. So, the Muslims bided their time and early in 1099, the news they most wanted to hear reached them. El Cid's health was failing. He was too weak to rise from his bed except for short periods of time. His faithful and beautiful wife Jimena spent most of her time at his bedside. She was afraid that if she left him, even for a few moments, he might die in her absence and she would be robbed of the chance to say her final farewell.

There was great rejoicing in

the Muslims' camp when this became known. At once, the Muslim army began to gather, ready to attack as soon as El Cid breathed his last.

El Cid knew what was happening and he felt great frustration and fury. ''What can I do?'' he thought. ''My people depend on me, and I am too sick to help them . . .''

El Cid shuddered as he realised what would happen once he was dead. It was easy to picture the scene — the ferocious Muslims sweeping through the streets, killing men, women and children, setting fire to the houses, destroying the churches and seizing all the treasure in the city.

''Somehow, I must save my people, I must!'' El Cid murmured.

Day by day, El Cid grew weaker but all the time, he struggled with the problem. At last, when he was almost too ill to think clearly any more, he decided on a plan. He told Jimena to call his captains to his bedside, and when they came, he told them what he wanted them to do.

Then, El Cid looked at Jimena.

"When I die, do not weep for me," he told her. Jimena, already in tears, nodded her head. "No one must know I am dead," El Cid whispered. "Not for a while, at least. Above all, the Muslims must not know it! Promise me, all of you, that you will do as I have commanded!"

"Yes, yes, we will!" Jimena replied. "Everything shall be done as you wish, my beloved husband!"

El Cid smiled. "Then Valencia will be saved!" he said.

A few hours later, El Cid died. Jimena kissed him for the last time then got to her feet, pale and red-eyed, but calm.

"You know what you must do now," Jimena told the captains, and as she had been told by El Cid, she hurried away to order the soldiers in Valencia to arm themselves and prepare for war.

"Beat the drums for battle!" Jimena ordered. "El Cid is coming to lead you to another great victory over the Muslims!"

The soldiers were mystified at first. This was the last thing they had expected. But they decided that El Cid must have recovered from his sickness, and was at this moment putting on his armour and his trusty sword, which was called Tizona. The soldiers became certain that this was so when they saw El Cid's white horse, Bavieca, being led from its stable and saddled.

Outside Valencia, the Muslims heard the drums beating and the clank of arms and armour inside the city. They heard the sudden cheering of crowds of people who surged into the streets to greet the columns of El Cid's soldiers as they moved towards the city gates.

"What's this?" the Muslims cried, alarmed and surprised. "Have the Christians gone mad? El Cid must be dead by now, yet they are cheering and joyful!"

At once, the Muslims scrambled to prepare for battle. They only just managed to get into their armour, grab their swords and spears and form up their battle lines when the great gates of Valencia swung slowly open. A single horseman galloped out, holding in one hand a large white banner with a brilliant red cross emblazoned on it. In his other hand, he held a mighty sword. Behind him, there followed hundreds of horsemen followed by a huge crowd of foot soldiers.

The lone horseman galloped closer, until he was near enough for the Muslims to recognise.

"It's El Cid!" they yelled in sudden fear. "El Cid is leading his army against us!"

It was undoubtedly El Cid. Every Muslim in Spain could recognise that stern face, that unwavering soldierly gaze and the tall, upright figure of the general who had conquered them over and over again. And behind him came what seemed like an enormous army. At least 70,000 men, or so the Muslims thought.

As the Christians came thundering towards them, the Muslims heard every man chanting: "Cid! Cid! Cid!" At the sound of this name, the Muslim soldiers panicked. They began to run, and their horsemen, likewise, turned and started to gallop away. Before long, the entire Muslim army was in flight, running away as fast as they could with the Christians in pursuit.

At last, when El Cid's captains were certain that the Muslims would not come back, they ordered their men to return to Valencia. They marched back, singing and yelling in triumph, to be greeted by wildly cheering crowds as they entered the city.

No one noticed that one of the captains had remained behind, holding onto the bridle of El Cid's horse Bavieca.

"This last victory is your greatest victory, my Lord Cid," the captain murmured, gazing at the stiff, unmoving figure sitting upright in Bavieca's saddle.

In all the excitement, no one, either Christian or Muslim, had seen that El Cid was firmly lashed into the saddle so that he could not fall off. The arms holding the banner and the sword were propped up by shafts of wood concealed beneath the sleeves of his chain-mail tunic. These had been El Cid's orders — that his captains dress him in his armour and place him on Bavieca's back so that he could lead his army into battle even after he was dead. By this means, El Cid planned to put heart into his own men and fear into the Muslims. He had succeeded brilliantly.

The captain pulled Bavieca's bridle and made the horse turn round. Then, sadly, but triumphantly, he led Bavieca, with the dead Cid sitting on its back away from Valencia. He was heading inland, into the Kingdom of Castile and the city of Burgos. There, El Cid had been born and there, according to his own orders, he wanted to be buried.

William Tell

"Hey, you! Come back at once, unless you want to be killed on the spot!"

William Tell knew that voice. It was harsh and loud. It sounded as if it belonged to a cruel man. Gritting his teeth with anger, William Tell went on striding across the square.

"Stop, I said!" roared the voice. "Or I swear I'll . . ."

William halted and turned on his heel. He glared across the square at Vogt Gessler, the fat, evil-looking man to whom the voice belonged. William's fingers tightened around the shaft of the crossbow he carried in his hand. How he longed to shoot one good bolt straight into Gessler's black heart!

Vogt Gessler, the Austrian governor of the Swiss canton of Uri, was a tyrant, as all Austrians were tyrants. The freedom-loving Swiss whose land they ruled so harshly seven hundred years ago hated all Austrians, but Gessler most of all. Gessler delighted in making the people of Uri suffer as much as possible. He sent his men to steal their food and turn them out of their homes. He took their money, or he imprisoned them and beat them up for no reason at all. The man was a fiend, with a soul as black as hell.

Now, the latest humiliation Gessler imposed upon the people was a hat set upon a pole in the centre of the town square at Altdorf: this, Gessler had proclaimed was the symbol of the mighty power of the Austrians, and everyone had to kneel before it.

The pole, with the ridiculous hat perched on top of it, stood only a short way from where William Tell stood now. He had walked right past it, for he absolutely refused to kneel before that or any other symbol of Austrian power.

Gessler was swaggering across the square towards him. "You swear to do what, Gessler?" William snarled as the Austrian approached. "Kill me? Put me in prison? You would have a riot on your hands within the hour! Remember who I am Gessler — and take care!"

Gessler knew who William Tell was all right! He was the greatest hero and the finest bowman in all Switzerland. Everyone, not just the people in the canton of Uri, looked up to him.

So, Gessler knew that if he laid a finger on William Tell, there were scores of Swiss who would be glad to kill him in order to avenge their hero.

Gessler decided to ignore William's words. Instead, he pointed to the pole in the square. "You have been ordered to kneel before that hat!" the Austrian growled. "You walked past it. This is an insult to the Emperor!"

William laughed. "The Emperor? That miserable creature? I would not let a hair of my head bend in honour to him!"

Gessler began to feel hot with anger. "Kneel before that

hat!'' he shouted. ''I command you!''

''Never!'' William replied stubbornly.

Before the infuriated Gessler could reply, William turned and stalked off, his head held high. Gessler watched the proud, straight-backed figure of the Swiss bowman and cursed and swore under his breath.

The impudence of the man, the sheer impudence! This was not the first time William Tell had openly defied Gessler and the Austrians.

''It must stop!'' Gessler raged. ''I must find some way to get the better of him!''

For days afterwards, Gessler could think of nothing else. He brooded over one plan after another until at last the very idea he wanted came into his head. ''What a splendid revenge I shall have!'' Gessler chortled.

Unable to wait a moment to put his plan into action, Gessler grabbed a quill pen and two pieces of parchment. On one parchment, he wrote a short, urgent message to his friend, the Governor of Zurich. On the second parchment, Gessler wrote out a proclamation.

That same afternoon, Gessler's proclamation, signed and sealed with a splendid red wax seal, appeared on the door of the church in Altdorf. At once, people began crowding round, wondering what the black-hearted Gessler wanted to inflict upon them now.

However, the proclamation contained no orders, as the people of Altdorf expected. Instead, it contained a challenge.

''Walther of Zurich, the greatest crossbowman in the world, arrives in Altdorf in three days' time,'' Gessler had written. ''It is well known that no Swiss bowman can match Walther for skill and accuracy with the crossbow, but any Swiss foolish enough to challenge him may do so. The people of Altdorf and all Switzerland will then see how puny their men are compared to a mighty Austrian warrior like Walther! So that all in Altdorf may witness Walther's triumph, everyone — men, women and children — is commanded to attend the contest in the square under pain of death!''

As Gessler expected, the people of Uri who read this proclamation were infuriated by the insult it contained. They rushed to William Tell to inform him of the contest. It was quite unnecessary, Gessler realised, to threaten everyone in Altdorf with death unless they attended, for everyone would want to come. Gessler just wanted to make sure, though, that William Tell brought his small son with him. That was a very important part of Gessler's plan.

Three days later, the entire population of Altdorf gathered in the town square. Gessler arrived with Walther, who had come speedily from Zurich at Gessler's urgent request. The Austrian crossbowman was a large man, with great muscle-bound arms. He was an extremely good shot and the best crossbowman in the Austrian army. The people of Altdorf, naturally, believed that William Tell was much better and they looked forward to seeing Walther well and truly beaten.

Walther positioned himself with his crossbow in the centre of the square, and when a fanfare of trumpets blew, the crowd fell silent. Gessler stepped forward.

''Who comes to challenge the best crossbowman in the world?'' he cried. ''Does anyone dare?''

At once, William Tell came out into the square, crossbow in hand. ''I dare!'' he cried in ringing

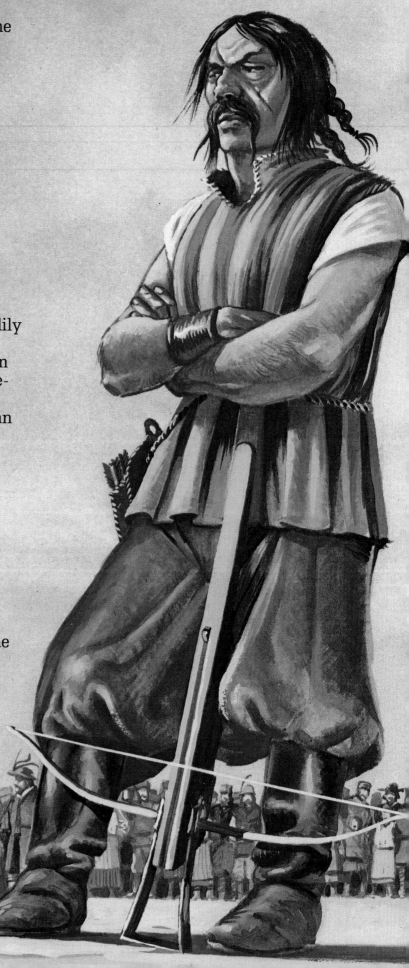

tones. ''Show me the target, and I will show you how a crossbow should be used. Come, what is the target?''

This was the moment Gessler had been waiting for. He nodded to three soldiers whom he had stationed close by and before anyone could stop them, they pushed into the crowd, grabbed William Tell's young son and pulled him out into the square.

William turned on Gessler in a fury. ''What is this, Gessler?'' he cried. ''What evil trick are you playing?''

Gessler smiled grimly. ''You asked what the target was!'' he said, pointing to William's son. ''The target is your own child!''

At this, screams and wails of shock and amazement sounded in the crowd. William Tell turned very pale. He knew he could not back down from the challenge now. That would bring him great dishonour. But to shoot at his own son! It was Gessler's most fiendish plot yet.

''You devil, Gessler! You shall roast in Hell for this!'' William cried. He was trembling violently half with fear, half with rage.

Gessler smiled again. ''I think not,'' he said. ''I am not asking you to shoot your son, just to shoot towards him. See!'' Gessler pulled a large red apple out of his pocket. ''This is what you shall aim for. The boy will be tied to that lime tree over there, and you will yourself place this apple on his head. If you are as good a crossbowman as people say you are, you and your son should have nothing to fear. But if not . . .''

Gessler chuckled wickedly. He had no need to say any more.

Still trembling, William Tell took the apple and after his son had been bound to the tree, placed it carefully on top of the boy's fair hair.

47

"Keep very still, my dearest boy," he whispered to him. "Do not flinch. Do not move, for if you do, my aim cannot be true!"

The boy attempted to smile.

"I will try, Father," he said in a small, frightened voice.

William kissed the boy farewell. Praying hard that fear of killing him would not spoil his aim, he walked back slowly across the square. A line had been marked for the crossbowmen to stand and shoot, and William put his foot on it. He raised his crossbow, and with tremendous effort managed to hold it steady. He took aim.

Everyone in the square had their eyes glued on William Tell, including Gessler.

"He will be too afraid to shoot straight," Gessler thought gleefully. "His son is sure to die!"

William looked along the shaft of his crossbow. He saw his son's small frightened face staring at him, and started to tremble. He struggled to control himself. Slowly, William raised the crossbow until the shaft and the bolt inside it were in line with the apple on top of his son's head. A second later, William pulled the bowstring and then swiftly closed his eyes. He could not bear to watch.

William Tell need not have worried. His aim was as perfect as always. The bolt sped through the air and plunged straight into the apple. It fell apart, in two neat, clean halves.

A tremendous cheer went up from the crowd and people began running across the square to congratulate William on his amazing marksmanship. They reached him to find him sobbing with relief.

Gessler was furious. His plan had failed completely. He turned and began to stalk angrily away from the square, taking Walther with him. Before he had gone far, William Tell called to him.

"Gessler! See this!" he cried. Gessler looked, to see William holding a second crossbow bolt in his hand. "If I had killed my son, Vogt Gessler" he growled at the Austrian, "this bolt would

48

have entered your wicked heart!
Here — take it." William tossed the
bolt towards Gessler who jumped
back quickly in case it hit him.
The crowd laughed. "Keep it as a
souvenir of this contest!"
William shouted as Gessler stalked
away. "I have plenty more, and I
swear that on the day we Swiss
drive the Austrians out of
Switzerland, one of them will be
specially reserved for you!"

Roland and Oliver

"I will never forgive Roland for this, never!" Ganelon muttered as he spurred his horse away from the camp of his commander, the Frankish King Charlemagne. Ganelon felt an enormous desire for revenge. He had always hated Roland, his stepson and the nephew of Charlemagne. Now, he hated him more than ever. Because of Roland, Ganelon was riding into great danger, perhaps to his death.

After seven years of victorious war against the Muslims in Spain, Charlemagne had grown weary of fighting. He wanted to make peace with Marsilion of Saragossa, the only Muslim king he had not overcome. Charlemagne decided to send an ambassador to Marsilion and Roland had suggested Ganelon. Charlemagne agreed.

Ganelon was furious, but he had to obey Charlemagne. It was a dangerous mission, for the Muslims were very violent and unpredictable

people.

Yet, the more Ganelon thought about it, the more he realised that perilous or not, this mission could give him the chance to get his revenge. "If I can persuade King Marsilion to help me," Ganelon mused, "I could get rid of Roland for ever!"

Despite his fears about the dangers of his journey, Ganelon reached Saragossa safely. At first, Marsilion and the Muslims were very suspicious of Ganelon, but eventually, they agreed to co-operate with him. In any case, the Muslims, too, wanted revenge, for they had suffered many dreadful defeats at the hands of the Franks.

"You must send hostages to Charlemagne, to show that you truly mean to make peace," Ganelon advised Marsilion.

Marsilion agreed to do so, and Ganelon went on: "When Charlemagne has your hostages, he will take his army home. But because he is a careful commander, he will not leave himself unprotected as he marches through the narrowest passes of the mountains of the Pyrenees. The pass at Roncevaux is

particularly dangerous. I am sure that Charlemagne will leave a force of his soldiers there to guard it!"

"But how will that help you get rid of your stepson Roland?" King Marsilion asked curiously.

"You will see," Ganelon replied with a wicked smile. "Just make sure your men are well hidden behind the rocks around the pass. I will do the rest!"

When Ganelon returned with the Muslim hostages and the news that Marsilion was willing to make peace, Charlemagne at once made preparations to return home to his kingdom. Charlemagne's great army set off, and moved slowly through the Pyrenees with great soaring peaks on either side and only narrow, winding mountain trails to follow. Their progress was slow, and the rumblings and clatterings of their carts could be heard a long way off. Marsilion's men heard the noise as they raced ahead to Roncevaux. As long as they kept the noise behind them, they knew they would reach Roncevaux before the Franks got there.

So it proved. When the

Frankish army reached Roncevaux, Marsilion's force lay concealed from view behind the rocks and in the crevices of the surrounding mountains.

"This is a perilous place," Charlemagne announced, just as Ganelon had guessed he would. "I will leave twenty thousand knights to guard the pass as my army moves through." Charlemagne looked round. "Who will command this rearguard?" he asked.

At once, before anyone else could speak, Ganelon came forward and said: "Roland, sire! Put Roland in command! He well deserves so important a task!"

Out of the corner of his eye, Ganelon saw Roland's face light up with excitement at his stepfather's suggestion. However, Charlemagne did not agree at first.

"Roland is a splendid soldier but he is too young and rash," the King replied. "It needs an older, more experienced man."

At this, though, Roland threw himself to his knees in front of Charlemagne.

"I beg you, sire," Roland cried. "Give me this command! I

swear I will prove worthy of it. I will defend the pass here at Roncevaux with my very life if I must!"

"Perfect!" thought Ganelon. "Roland is conspiring at his own death." Out loud, Ganelon begged Charlemagne: "Heed my stepson's request, gracious sire. After all, Roland honoured me with a great task, as ambassador to King Marsilion. I would return the favour!"

Confronted by Ganelon's insistence and Roland's eagerness, Charlemagne at last gave in.

"Very well, then," he said, "but Oliver and the Twelve Peers will remain behind with Roland."

Oliver was Roland's sensible and stout-hearted friend. The Twelve Peers were the bravest and most experienced Frankish knights. Charlemagne hoped that between them they could stop Roland from doing anything foolish. And if they were in danger, Roland could always blow on his horn and summon Charlemagne and his army to his aid.

When Charlemagne and his army had moved off, Roland set about disposing his forces. Some he set to guard the pass itself, others he sent to watch on the mountain ridges above.

The Muslims lay low until they were sure Charlemagne was some distance away. Then, all at once, Roland and Oliver were startled to hear the sound of a thousand trumpets echoing through the mountains. The sound echoed back and forth between the peaks, and before the echo had died away, there came the sound of horses galloping and the fearful war cries of the Muslim hordes.

Intensely alarmed, Oliver scrambled up a steep rise by the side of the path, to a point where he could scan the ground on the other side. There, to his horror, he saw the great mass of Marsilion's warriors. Thousands of burnished helmets gleamed in the mountain sunshine. Thousands of spears, shields and swords glinted menacingly in the clear bright light. And all of them were moving rapidly towards the pass at Roncevaux.

Oliver hurried down to where Roland was standing. "There are at least 100,000 of them," he told Roland fearfully. "We will be overwhelmed. I beg you, Roland, sound your horn now. Summon Charlemagne back!"

Oliver was appalled when Roland refused. "I will summon no aid," Roland maintained stubbornly. "If we cannot throw back the Muslims ourselves, we deserve to die as cowards!"

A terrible despair took hold of Oliver. Charlemagne had been right not to want the incautious Roland to command his rearguard. Twice more, Oliver begged Roland to summon Charlemagne. Twice more, Roland refused. It was too late now, in any case. Marsilion's Muslims were thundering closer and closer. There was nothing to do now but confront them and fight to the death.

A few moments later, the Muslims were upon them. Roland and his knights plunged into the battle, slashing about them with their swords and spears.

Roland drove his spear through a Muslim's shield and helmet with one mighty thrust. Then, he forced his way into a group of Muslims and brought down fifteen of them before the shaft of his spear broke into pieces. Nothing daunted, Roland grasped Durendal, his great sword, and flung himself towards a Muslim warrior, killing the man and his horse with one swift stroke.

Before long, only two thousand Muslims were left alive. The rest had fallen before the thrusting spears, slashing swords and hammering blows of the Franks. Although many of his own men had also been killed, Roland was sure that he had won a great victory. He was just about to raise Durendal to proclaim his triumph when, suddenly, the sound of trumpets reached his ears.

Instantly, Roland knew what it was. "A second Muslim army!" he gasped.

Seconds later, the slopes above the pass at Roncevaux seemed to be covered in a fresh crowd of Muslim warriors. Like a great tide, they swamped down onto Roland and the exhausted, battle-stained

the world.

Roland put the mouthpiece of the horn to his lips but just then Oliver rushed up and stopped him.

"It would be to our dishonour if you called for help now!" Oliver shouted angrily. "Better to die here than live in disgrace!"

"No, I MUST summon Charlemagne now," Roland replied. "If I had

survivors of his force.

Roland and the Franks hurled themselves against this new, mighty enemy, but they were soon close to being overwhelmed. One Muslim killed five of the Twelve Peers, another two Peers fell and soon only sixty Frankish knights were left alive.

Roland looked round with pain in his heart to see the bodies of his men littering the ground. At last, he realised he must blow his horn and summon Charlemagne. Charlemagne must be far away by now but Roland's horn was a special, magic instrument. It was covered in gold and precious stones and its high, clear note could be heard further away than any other horn in

listened to you and done so before, this disaster would never have happened!"

Before Oliver could say any more, Roland put the horn to his lips and blew with all the strength he possessed. Harder and harder he blew until, suddenly, he felt a snap and a dreadful pain in his head. All at once, blood was flowing from his mouth. Roland had blown with such force that a vein in the side of his head had burst.

The sound of the horn soared up into the sky and over the mountains, echoing on and on until it reached the ears of Charlemagne, thirty leagues (ninety miles) away. Charlemagne started up in his saddle in great alarm.

"Dear God!" he cried. "Roland has been attacked!" Charlemagne turned the head of his horse to ride back swiftly to Roland's aid. "Pray God we may reach him in time," he muttered fearfully.

Ganelon, hearing this, gave a derisive laugh. "Do not trouble yourself, sire!" he scoffed. "It is only one of Roland's tricks. There is no attack. Come, let us get on — we are still far from home!"

In that moment, Charlemagne realised what Ganelon had done.

"You have betrayed Roland! You have betrayed me!" the King roared. "Seize him!" he ordered.

A group of Frankish knights, as infuriated as Charlemagne at Ganelon's treachery, leapt upon him, bound him and flung him into one of the baggage carts.

"You shall die for this foul betrayal!" Charlemagne promised Ganelon. Charlemagne kept his promise, for Ganelon was afterwards put to death.

Now, the whole Frankish army was turning and heading back the way they had come. They rode as fast as the rocky terrain and the winding mountain paths would allow them. From time to time, the Franks heard Roland's horn echoing across the mountains. Charlemagne's trumpeters blew in reply, but a night and a day passed before they could be heard at Roncevaux. The Muslims, seeing Charlemagne was returning, fled in panic. They left Charlemagne to discover a dreadful scene of tragedy and death.

The battlefield at Roncevaux was thickly littered with the corpses of men and horses. Oliver lay dead, his face ghostly white. A Muslim spear had struck him in the back and pierced right through

his body to his chest. All Twelve Peers had been killed. As Charlemagne looked slowly round, he realised that all the knights he had left with Roland were lying dead before him.

Then the grieving King of the Franks found Roland. He was lying on a grassy bank close to a rock. Upon the rock, Charlemagne saw three deep sword-cuts. Beneath Roland's body lay his beautiful bejewelled horn and his sword Durendal. Knowing that he was dying, for he had lost so much blood from continuously blowing his horn, Roland had tried to destroy Durendal by striking it on the rock. Durendal had remained unbroken, however, and Roland had not had

the strength to try a fourth time. Instead, to keep Durendal from falling into Muslim hands, Roland had placed it on the ground. Then, he had lain upon it, and there, he had died.

Charlemagne tore his beard with grief. He wept and called out the names of his dead knights. He swore he would have his revenge. Because it was nearly dark now, Charlemagne knelt and prayed that the Sun would stand still in the sky so that he could pursue the fleeing Muslims. Charlemagne's prayer was granted. Only when he and his army had killed all the Muslims and left their bodies strewn along the road to Saragossa or in the river nearby, did the Sun set and the night fall.

Androclus and the Lion

Androclus shivered as another icy drop of water dripped onto his face. He looked up at the cave roof above his head. Another drop was forming there. Androclus moved aside. The drop plopped down onto the rocky shelf beside him.

Androclus drew his cloak round his shoulders and wrapped his arms round himself, trying to keep warm. It was no use trying to sleep in this cave, he thought miserably. Still, the soldiers who were out hunting for him would not find him in here, and maybe the lions would

not find him either. At least, Androclus hoped so. The last thing he wanted was for a ferocious lion to come into the cave. The animal would probably be hungry, and then . . . Androclus did not want to think about what would happen then.

''Still,'' Androclus thought, trying to cheer himself up, ''at least I'm free now.''

At least his cruel master, Publius Sirius would not be able to give him a beating today and then send him off, sore and aching, to do a day's hard labour in his vineyards. Androclus had hated his master ever since the day Publius had bought him in the slave market in Rome.

Four years passed before Androclus managed to escape from Publius's farm. Now, hiding inside the cave, Androclus thought over the plans he had made to get away from Italy. He would stay in the cave till it grew dark. The soldiers Publius had sent to catch him would not be looking for him at night. Then, Androclus planned to leave the cave, and make his way to the coast. There, he hoped to find a boat and sail back to his home in Greece.

Androclus looked at the shafts of light that were coming into the cave. The sun seemed to be low in the sky now. It might be dark soon.

''I must have a look,'' Androclus murmured. He peered out of the cave entrance. ''Good,'' he thought, seeing the deep blue of the sky, ''an hour or so, and the sun would set.''

Suddenly, as he was turning to go back into the cave, Androclus saw the lion. His skin prickled with fright, and he gave a start as a low, growling roar came from the lion's throat. It stood only a few feet away from him, a powerful creature, with a flowing mane, and a great swishing tail. There was something strange, though. Surely the lion would have noticed Androclus by now?

However, it seemed to be more concerned with its front paw, which it was holding off the ground and licking from time to time. Every now and then, the lion gave a sort of whining howl, as if it was in pain.

When Androclus looked at the paw, he saw why. It was very swollen and rather black in colour. Quite obviously, it hurt a great deal. Androclus felt great pity for the wounded creature. He wanted to help, but it was a great risk.

Androclus was very soft-hearted. He loved animals, and could not bear to see even a fierce lion suffering. His mind was made up quickly.

Moving carefully, Androclus approached the lion. The lion was sitting down now, still whining and still licking its paw. As it heard Androclus creep closer, it looked up. Androclus saw that instead of the wild, ferocious glare lions usually had, this one was looking at him pleadingly, as if it wanted help.

Slowly, very slowly, Androclus stretched out his hand and stroked the lion's mane. To his relief, the lion let him do it.

There was a large, sharp spike embedded in one of the pads. It looked like a large thorn, or a piece of metal.

"That's got to come out," said Androclus. It was best to do it quickly. Androclus grabbed the spike and pulled hard. As he did

"That's a bad paw you've got there, poor old fellow," Androclus murmured. "Let's have a look at it — all right, I won't hurt you!"

The lion gave a howl as Androclus touched its paw. For one terrible moment, Androclus thought it was going to attack him. But it just looked sadly at Androclus and the howl became a whine. Androclus carefully lifted the lion's front leg and looked closely at the injured paw.

so, the lion gave a deafening roar.

Androclus went back into the cave to fetch some water from one of the many puddles that lay on the floor inside. Androclus tore his cloak into long strips, soaked them in ice-cold water and went outside again.

For the next few minutes Androclus bathed the swollen paw and wrapped it up in the long wet strips of cloth. All the time, the lion watched him and now and then let out a sound rather like a purr. After a while, the swelling in the paw seemed to go down a bit and it did not look quite so black as before.

Androclus felt thankful, too, to see that there was less pain in the lion's eyes.

Finally, Androclus made a pad out of one of the wet strips of cloth, placed it over the wound and then wrapped the paw in another strip.

"That will protect it until it heals," he told the lion and in a strange way, Androclus thought, the lion seemed to understand.

The lion was obviously feeling a lot better. It got up on three legs and began to hobble around. Then, it hobbled forward a few steps and before long, the lion was moving along the rocky path, away from where Androclus stood watching him. Then, the lion began to move more quickly until he disappeared over a small hillock.

What Androclus did not know as he watched the lion was that three soldiers were watching *him.* They had spotted Androclus outside the cave and crept up unseen while he was tending the lion. Now, the soldiers were hiding behind rocks further up the hill, waiting until the lion disappeared from sight.

"All right," one of the soldiers muttered to the others when the lion had gone. "Let's grab him!"

Androclus heard the soldiers as they scrambled from behind the rock, but by the time he started to run away, it was too late. One of the soldiers grabbed Androclus round the waist and threw him onto the rocky ground. The other two held him down, while the soldier tied his wrists together with rope.

Androclus felt like weeping. It was so unjust that his act of kindness towards the lion should end like this.

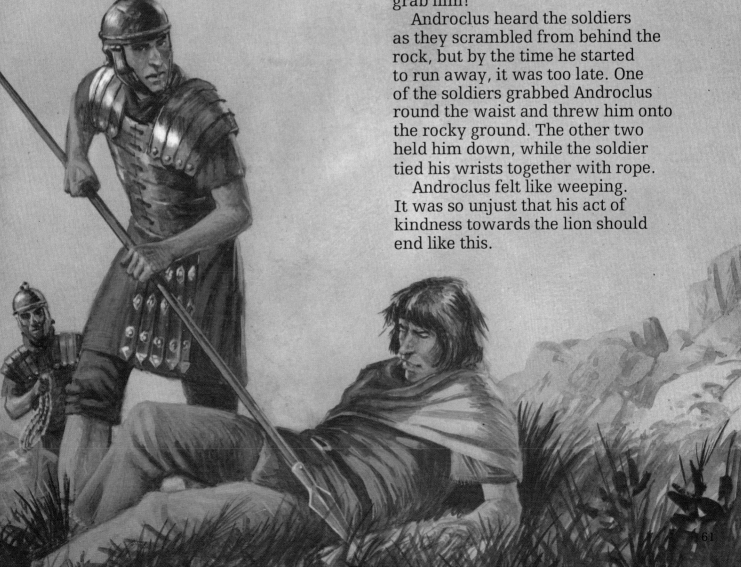

One of the soldiers gave Androclus a rough push.

"Your master Publius Sirius wants to see you," he told Androclus. "He's got a very special punishment for runaway slaves!"

"What is it? What's going to happen to me?" Androclus gasped, remembering how cruel Publius Sirius was.

The soldiers laughed. "You'll see!" they sneered. "And when you do, you'll be sorry you ever thought of running away."

Three weeks later, Androclus sat on the floor of a large underground cellar with his hands chained to a ring that was sunk into the stone wall. Nearby sat another man, chained in the same way, and next to him, another and another. From above their heads, they could all hear the crowd chattering and laughing as they took their seats around the amphitheatre. From the excitement in their voices it was clear that the crowd expected good, bloodthirsty sport today. After all, it wasn't every day that runaway slaves and ferocious lions were put into the arena together. Androclus had heard that Emperor Tiberius himself was coming to watch.

This was certainly a special punishment, just as Publius Sirius had planned. This time, Androclus thought grimly, there was no hope of escape.

There was a sudden burst of cheering from above, in the amphitheatre. "The Emperor's arrived," the man next to Androclus whispered. "It won't be long now!"

A few moments later, the bolts on the cellar door were drawn back and the door creaked open. A troop of soldiers marched in and started unchaining Androclus and the other slaves. Then, they were pushed into the centre of the cellar and a large grille at the end was pulled up. Beyond it lay the sand covered arena, the eagerly awaiting crowd of spectators — and the lions. Androclus felt a sharp push in his back and he stumbled forward. With the other slaves, he emerged into the brilliant sunshine that filled the arena. As the crowd spotted them, they let out a great yell of excitement.

There was a scraping sound from across the arena and a grille at the opposite end moved up. At once, ten or twelve lions came bounding out and started racing across the sand to where the slaves stood, petrified with fear.

The first lion to reach them leapt upwards and Androclus got a quick glimpse of the underneath of its belly as it landed on a slave and knocked him to the ground. Androclus and the rest of the slaves started to run, out into the centre or round the sides of the arena.

The crowd shouted and clapped as they watched. They laughed at those slaves who tried to climb the walls in an attempt to escape, only to have lions leap up at them and pull them back.

Suddenly, Androclus saw a lion leap towards him. He tried to get out of the way, but the great animal was upon him before he could do so. Androclus felt the hot pain of the lion's claws tearing into his arm as he fell. Any moment now, and Androclus would feel the lion's sharp, curved fangs sinking into his flesh . . .

But nothing like that occurred. Instead, to Androclus' amazement, the lion started licking the scratches on his arm. The crowd saw what was happening, and their shouts of excitement turned to shouts of astonishment. And no wonder. When the lion had finished licking Androclus' arm, it lay down next to him and put its paw across his chest, as if to protect him.

Even the Emperor Tiberius was on his feet, mouth open with amazement. Nothing like this had ever been seen in the amphitheatre

before. Androclus put his hands up and turned the lion's face towards him.

"I know you!" Androclus said. "And you haven't forgotten me!"

The lion purred as Androclus lifted its paw and looked at it. There, sure enough, was a small round hole in one of the pads. This was the lion Androclus had tended at the cave. Now, it was showing how grateful it was. Not only had the lion refused to kill Androclus, but it was growling fiercely at other lions who came near him.

The whole amphitheatre was in an uproar now. The Emperor ordered the animal keepers to drive the other lions back into their cellar. The slaves who were still unharmed stood and wept with relief at their unexpected escape from death.

Androclus got to his feet, and dusted the sand off his tunic. The lion sat meekly beside him, looking up at him with adoring eyes. Everyone in the crowd was clapping, as if Androclus was a great hero. Even the Emperor joined in, and a tremendous cheering broke out as Androclus walked round the ring with the lion following him like a faithful dog.

Emperor Tiberius was so amused that he gave Androclus his freedom.

"A man who can tame the wildest of beasts cannot be a slave!" the Emperor told the delighted Androclus.

Androclus was even more delighted when the Emperor let him keep the lion as his own. Afterwards the two of them became well known in Rome, for wherever Androclus went, the lion went, too. No one was afraid to meet them in the street, even when Androclus did not put the lion on a lead. After all, wasn't it the tamest lion ever seen in Rome?

Daedalus and Icarus

"Icarus! Wake up! Wake up!"
Daedalus was sorry that he had to
shake his small son so roughly, but
it was important that the boy woke
up quickly. He and his father were
in great danger. Any moment now,
King Minos' guards would be
outside the door. Daedalus shook
his son again.

"Come on, Icarus!" he cried.
"Wake up!"

"By all the gods, why did the
boy have to sleep so soundly?"

Daedalus muttered. But then,
everyone in the palace of Minos had
been sound asleep the previous
night when that cunning Prince
Theseus of Athens entered the
labyrinth and killed the Minotaur
imprisoned there. Everyone was
still fast asleep when Theseus
sailed away with the fourteen young
Athenians who had come with him to
the island of Crete. Moreover,
Theseus had taken Princess Ariadne,
King Minos' daughter, with him.

Next morning, when the king discovered what had happened, there was uproar throughout the entire palace. And the first person the enraged king had called for was Daedalus, the craftsman who had made the labyrinth in which the Minotaur was kept.

"Where is that wretched Daedalus? Where is he?" King Minos raged. "I will tear him apart, I will burn him with hot coals, I will fling him off the cliff! The wretch, the liar! He told me that no one could get out of the labyrinth alive! Now the Minotaur is dead and Theseus has escaped with my hostages and my daughter!"

Daedalus heard the shouting and raving coming from the king's rooms and realised that the time had come to leave Crete — and to leave immediately! It was only a matter of time before Minos' soldiers came to arrest Daedalus — and drag him to the king.

Daedalus shook Icarus' shoulder again, more violently this time. Icarus opened his eyes and murmured sleepily: "What is it, Father? Why do I have to wake up now?"

"We have to escape, my son," Daedalus whispered urgently. "I will explain why later. But if we don't go now, it could mean death for both of us!"

Icarus was wide awake now. His father was obviously worried, very worried indeed.

"You know you've always wanted to fly?" Daedalus said. "Well, now's your chance."

Daedalus went over to a large box in the corner of the room. Somehow, Daedalus had always known that one day, he and Icarus might have to escape from Crete. So he had made wings from bird feathers, and set aside four balls of wax with which to fix them.

Now, Daedalus lifted the wings from the box and worked quickly but carefully to attach the smaller pair onto Icarus' back. "Poor Icarus," Daedalus thought, "he believes it's all a game."

This was the second time he and his son had been forced to escape from danger together. The first time, Daedalus had had to flee from his native city of Athens after he had thrown his nephew, Perdix, over a cliff in a fit of jealousy. Although Perdix was only a young boy, he was already a very clever inventor and craftsman, much cleverer, people said, than Daedalus was himself. As Perdix tumbled over the cliff, the goddess Athene had saved him from death by turning him into a partridge.

Even so, Daedalus was afraid of what would happen when his crime was discovered, so he took Icarus and fled by night to the island of Crete. There, King Minos had given him shelter. Now, Daedalus and Icarus had to run away again.

At last, Daedalus was satisfied with Icarus' wings. They were well fixed and should carry him safely across the sea. However, as Daedalus fixed his own, larger wings, onto his own back, he had a strong warning for Icarus.

"Remember your wings are stuck on with wax," Daedalus said. "Wax melts in heat, so take care not to fly too near the Sun, or your wings will fall off! You understand, don't you, Icarus?"

"Oh yes, father, of course I understand!" Icarus replied, only half-listening.

Icarus was too excited at the thought of flying like a bird to think of anything else. The wings on his back were made of beautiful snow-white feathers, just like those of the birds he had often watched flying over the island. Already, Icarus felt very proud of them. With his great white wings, he would fly far better and further than his cousin Perdix, who had become a partridge. Partridges were only small grey birds, Icarus thought scornfully.

Daedalus looked at the eager, excited face of his young son and prayed that no harm would befall him.

"Just follow me," he told Icarus. "Don't fly any higher than I do, and you will be all right!"

Just then, Daedalus heard an unmistakable sound in the corridor outside. The tramp, tramp, tramp of soldier's feet marching speedily towards his rooms.

"Quickly, Icarus!" Daedalus

spoke urgently as he led his son onto the balcony. "Jump up into the air when I tell you, and don't look down!" Daedalus gave Icarus a quick, anxious kiss, then said: "Now, Icarus! Jump!"

Icarus did as he was told and together with his father, he rose slowly into the air. The wings attached to his back moved up and down, and before long, Icarus and Daedalus were flying high above the grounds of the palace, over the golden sandy beaches along the shore and out to sea. The Sun shone warm and bright all round

them, the sea below sparkled and the air felt fresh and clean on their faces as they flew along.

Every now and then, Daedalus looked round anxiously, to ensure Icarus was behind him. Every time, Icarus waved excitedly at his father. He was enjoying himself hugely.

An hour or so passed, and below there was nothing to be seen but the sea and an occasional fishing boat. The island of Crete had long ago disappeared below the horizon. By this time, Icarus was getting a bit bored with just flying along behind his father. He wanted to do as the birds did — swoop downwards, turn and zoom upwards, perhaps move sideways in the wind currents that were blowing around him.

"I'll try it!" Icarus decided. He glanced ahead to see that his father was not looking, then spread

his wings out straight. He waggled
them a little at the tips and
found himself flying sideways, just
like the birds.

"It works!" Icarus cried,
greatly thrilled.

Next, Icarus leaned downwards
and swooped for a second or two,
then zoomed upwards again so that
he was once more flying behind
Daedalus. Icarus could almost
believe now that he had never been
anything but a flying creature.

Just then, a flock of birds

came zooming up, right in front of
Icarus. They were making for
greater heights before levelling
out again. Icarus followed them.
Up, up, he went, hardly noticing
that it was becoming hotter and
hotter as he got higher and higher.
The Sun was shining more and more
brightly, but Icarus did not stop.

"I can fly as high as the
birds," he said. "I know I can!"

Suddenly, far below, Daedalus
turned round yet again, to make
sure Icarus was following him. He
found the sky behind him was
empty. Greatly alarmed, Daedalus
looked up and saw, to his horror,
that Icarus was nothing but a small
dot high in the sky. "Icarus!

Icarus!" Daedalus cried out in
great fear. "Icarus, come back!"
    But Icarus was far too high to
hear him. Besides, he was feeling
rather faint from the heat of the
Sun. He also grew more and more
frightened as the wind currents
took hold of him and shot him
upwards at tremendous speed. Then,
without warning, Icarus felt two
burning patches on his back. The
wax! It was melting! Suddenly,
instead of flying, Icarus was
falling. Below him as he fell, he
saw his two wings being thrown
about by the wind. They had come

off, just as his father had warned him!

Down, down Icarus plunged, faster and faster. Daedalus had been turning this way and that, trying to see where his son was, when the boy fell past him, arms flailing wildly, hands trying to clutch at the air. Daedalus went cold with fear and grief. He was helpless. All he could do was to watch Icarus falling away from him, getting smaller and smaller until a splash of foam in the sea below marked the spot where he plunged into the water.

"Icarus, my son, my son!" Daedalus moaned. A dreadful ache entered his heart, for he realised the boy could not have survived such a long fall into the sea.

Tears began to stream from Daedalus' eyes. He knew he had to find Icarus, but he dreaded finding that he was dead. And Icarus WAS dead. That was all too clear to Daedalus as he flew down close to the level of the sea. He found Icarus' limp body floating on the surface. The boy's face was terribly white and his eyes were closed. Floating nearby were the wings which had fallen from his back.

The weeping Daedalus gently lifted Icarus out of the water. There was a small rocky island not far away. Daedalus flew to it and landed on a small patch of sand on the shore. For a few moments, Daedalus was unable to do anything but hold Icarus close to him and weep disconsolately. At last, though, Daedalus realised that Icarus would have to be buried. With a grieving heart, he began to cover the boy with rocks and stones

from the sea shore.

There were many birds about on the island and a small group of them perched on a rock nearby, as if they were watching Daedalus. One of them suddenly chirruped and looking up, Daedalus saw it was a partridge.

A partridge! thought Daedalus. He looked more closely at the grey bird and remembered how his nephew Perdix had been changed into a partridge by Athene. Perhaps this partridge, looking at him now, was Perdix?

"If you are," Daedalus wept, "you will see how my crime against you has been avenged!"

Sir Gawain and the Green Knight

Suddenly, there was a mighty crash and a bang. Then, the thundering of iron hooves racing across the stone floor — and all at once, the great doors of the banqueting hall at Camelot Castle burst open. A huge man came galloping in on an enormous horse, and drew to a halt in the middle of the room.

Startled, King Arthur and his Knights jumped up from their seats at the Round Table. They stared speechlessly at the strange intruder.

He was all green, green from head to foot. His jerkin and cloak were green, his spurs were green, his hair and beard and skin were green. Even his horse was green.

"Which of you is the leader of this gathering?" the intruder boomed.

King Arthur stepped forward. "Who wishes to speak with him?" he demanded proudly.

"I am the mighty Green Knight of the North!" came the reply. "I have come to Camelot to see for myself whether all I have heard of this place is true!"

"And what have you heard?" King Arthur wanted to know.

"That this castle is the home of the bravest knights and the mightiest and most gracious king!" the Green Knight replied. He looked round rather disdainfully. "But now I am here, it seems that you are nothing but weaklings and beardless youths! I could kill every one of you with one stroke of my axe!"

At this, several Knights jumped up and drew their swords, ready there and then to kill this impudent intruder.

Arthur put up his hand to restrain them. He turned to the Green Knight. "You have made a great boast, sir," said the King. "You must prove it! You have spoken disdainfully of my Knights.

For that, they are honour bound to challenge you!"

The Green Knight threw back his great head and laughed loudly. "There is no Knight of yours who would dare take up my challenge!" he boasted.

"I will do so, whatever it may be!" It was the young, impetuous Sir Gawain, one of the most daring of Arthur's Knights. "What is your challenge?" Sir Gawain cried. "Speak!"

73

The Green Knight leaned over and took from the side of his saddle a huge green axe. Its blade was at least twice the length of a man's hand and its finely sharpened edge winked and sparkled in the torchlight that shone from all round the walls.

"I challenge you to exchange blow for blow with me with this great axe of mine!" said the Green Knight. "I will kneel here, on the floor and receive the first blow. Only remember this," the Knight continued menacingly. "You must swear on your honour to meet me next Christmastide and, unarmed, receive the second blow from me!"

At this, there was a gasp from all round the banqueting hall. The Green Knight must be a madman! That axe of his could slice through the head of an ox. Everyone including Sir Gawain, was staring at the Green Knight in amazement and disbelief, and he mistook their moment of silence for fear. He laughed scornfully.

"As I thought," he said. "You are cowards every one — my challenge is too great for you!"

Sir Gawain's face turned red with fury. "This fellow's insults are more than I can bear!" he cried. "I accept your challenge!"

The Green Knight gave a grim smile as he swung his leg over the saddle and dropped down to the floor. He was a giant — half as tall again as Sir Gawain. All the same, Sir Gawain was not deterred.

"Give me the axe," he demanded. Gawain took the axe, and tested it by swinging it to and fro a few times.

"I am ready," Sir Gawain said at length. "Are you prepared for the first blow, Sir Knight?"

In answer, the Green Knight knelt down on the floor, drew his long hair aside so that his neck was exposed and bent his head forward.

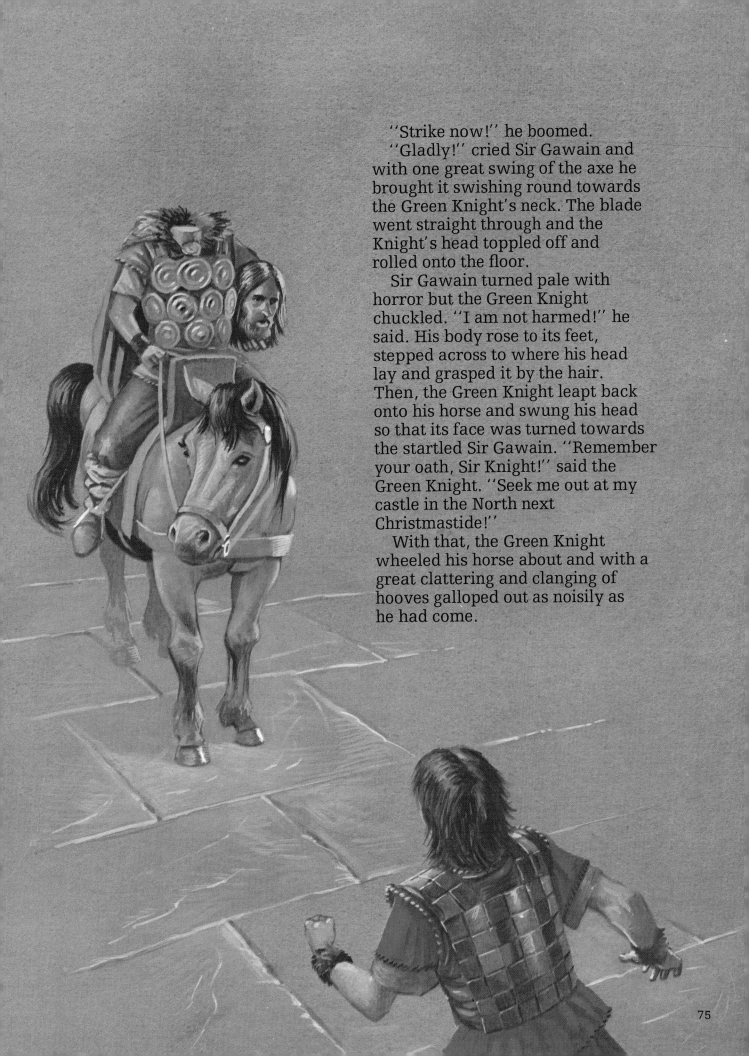

"Strike now!" he boomed.

"Gladly!" cried Sir Gawain and with one great swing of the axe he brought it swishing round towards the Green Knight's neck. The blade went straight through and the Knight's head toppled off and rolled onto the floor.

Sir Gawain turned pale with horror but the Green Knight chuckled. "I am not harmed!" he said. His body rose to its feet, stepped across to where his head lay and grasped it by the hair. Then, the Green Knight leapt back onto his horse and swung his head so that its face was turned towards the startled Sir Gawain. "Remember your oath, Sir Knight!" said the Green Knight. "Seek me out at my castle in the North next Christmastide!"

With that, the Green Knight wheeled his horse about and with a great clattering and clanging of hooves galloped out as noisily as he had come.

The following December, Sir Gawain set out from Camelot to seek the castle of the Green Knight. The way there was long and hard, and the weather raw and icy cold. Sir Gawain shivered constantly. Many times when snow blizzards were blowing all round him and the wind seemed to slice into his very bones, he wished he was back in Camelot.

It was only a passing thought, though. Sir Gawain fully intended to keep his strange bargain with the Green Knight. It was, however, curious that Sir Gawain should meet so many people on the road who tried to divert him from his purpose.

First, there was the splendidly clad nobleman who stopped him along the road and offered to entertain him at his castle nearby.

''There are great fires there to warm you,'' the nobleman promised. ''And a great feast, with wine unlimited! After the feast, you may rest in a bed covered in soft feathers.''

Sir Gawain thanked the nobleman, but refused his offer. ''No, kind sir,'' he told him. ''I am bound by my oath to meet the Green

Knight at his castle.''

Sir Gawain rode on, still freezing cold, and now, very hungry. He met the huntsman next. The huntsman hailed him and, like the nobleman, seemed very hospitable and generous.

''The castle of the Green Knight is far away, Sir Gawain!'' the huntsman told him. ''Surely you would rather come hunting with me and my friends? It is warm, exciting sport and there are plenty of deer and wild pigs to be caught hereabouts! Afterwards, we can have a great feast! What say you, Sir Gawain?''

Again, Sir Gawain refused. ''I thank you, sir. Your offer is kind,'' he replied. ''But I am bound by my oath to meet the Green Knight at his castle.''

Next, a knight appeared on the road, clad in full armour and obviously on his way to a tournament. The knight offered to take Sir Gawain with him so that they could test their fighting skills against each other and afterwards feast and talk round a roaring fire. But again, Gawain refused, and resolutely journeyed on towards the castle of the Green Knight.

At long last, the castle came
in sight. It was, of course, all
green. Its high towers and great
battlements made beautiful patterns
against the whitish-grey winter
sky. Sir Gawain rode into the
courtyard just as the sky was
beginning to grow dark. It was
Christmas Eve.

The Green Knight was there,
waiting for him. His head was back
on his shoulders again, with no
sign of the axe-stroke which had
severed his neck the Christmas
before.

"Welcome!" cried the Green
Knight, grinning gleefully at Sir
Gawain. "Let us to our business
straight away! I have been
impatient this last year, waiting
for this moment!"

The Green Knight was just as
terrible as Sir Gawain remembered
him, and his great green axe looked
as mighty and as sharp as before.
Silently, Sir Gawain murmured his
prayers as he followed the Green
Knight into the castle.

They reached the hall and the Green Knight pointed to a spot on the stone floor. ''Kneel there, Sir Gawain,'' he instructed. ''Here is where I answer the blow you gave me last Christmastide!''

With one last prayer on his lips, Sir Gawain knelt down, pushed his hair aside and bent his head forward.

''Make ready to strike,'' Sir Gawain told the Green Knight in a firm, clear voice. ''I am a Knight of the Round Table and I shall keep my vow to you, even if it costs me my life! Unlike you, I cannot replace my head when it falls to your axe! Come, sir, strike!''

The Green Knight lifted up the axe and swung it swiftly towards Sir Gawain's neck. Sir Gawain felt the rush of air it made. But the blade did not touch him. The Knight stopped it a finger's breadth away from Sir Gawain's neck.

Sir Gawain looked up, curious and startled.

''You are playing games with me!'' he accused the Green Knight. ''Come, it is not chivalrous to act so!''

Then, he noticed that the Green Knight was smiling at him, not disdainfully as he had seen him smile before, but with a friendly, even admiring look on his all-green face. The Knight placed his great hand under Sir Gawain's elbow and raised him to his feet.

"No, I am playing no game — only testing your courage and honour!" said the Green Knight quietly. "You did not flinch from my axe-blade just now. That took great courage. When I set all manner of temptations on the road between here and Camelot to divert you from your purpose, you refused all of them, even though you were cold and tired and hungry. That takes a truly honourable spirit!"

Sir Gawain gasped. "So it was you!" he cried. "Why, sir, you tempted me with the sweetest comforts any knight could ask for!"

"Then you shall enjoy them all now," the Green Knight smiled. "I have achieved my task, set me by Merlin, to make sure that King Arthur and his Knights are still the bravest and most honourable knights in Britain! You have certainly proved that they are, and now, Sir Gawain, we shall feast, we shall hunt and tomorrow there is a tournament, here at my castle. And tonight, you may sleep in comfort! You have well deserved it!"